Help!

My

dog

can't

stop

farting

Help!
My
dog
can't
stop
farting

Tony De Saulles

■SCHOLASTIC

For Twiggy
Sit… Good girl!

Scholastic Children's Books,
Commonwealth House, 1-19 New Oxford Street,
London WC1A 1NU, UK

A division of Scholastic Ltd
London ~ New York ~ Toronto ~ Sydney ~ Auckland
Mexico City ~ New Delhi ~ Hong Kong

Published in the UK by Scholastic Ltd, 2002

Text and illustrations copyright © Tony De Saulles, 2002

ISBN 0 439 99369 5

All rights reserved
Typeset by Falcon Oast Graphic Art Ltd, East Hoathly, Sussex
Printed by Cox & Wyman Ltd, Reading Berks

2 4 6 8 10 9 7 5 3 1

Contents

From Bad to Worse

Last year was not a happy time for us. Bad things kept happening. It was one lousy problem after another and by Christmas even Dad was stressed.

"Life can be cruel!" he sighed. "First the giant flea crisis, then the missing snake episode and last week the 'goldfish down the loo' incident. The world's gone crazy!"

Then the worst thing of all happened. A new veterinary surgery opened in Clover Street. It was big, bright and totally hi-tech. Basically, loads trendier. It's not like we were jealous, but they were pinching Dad's customers!

"I don't believe it!" Dad groaned, raising his eyes to the ceiling. "I mean, I'm a good vet, it's taken years to build up my surgery and now look what's happened! Some of my best clients enticed away with the promise of free flea collars. Even Mrs Arkwright and her poodles have abandoned me. One glance at that 'Cut-price Claw Clipping' poster was enough to win her over. This is a small town, there isn't room for both of us."

I racked my brains trying to think of some way to help and so did my big brother Zak. He's 13 and although he's not a brilliant artist like me, he is dead brainy and has ace ideas. He says that when he's older he'll make megabucks on the Internet. So I try to be nice to him just in case he really does.

That evening Dad was writing some business letters.

"Nobody writes letters any more!" Zak scoffed, "You've got to stop living in the past. Get into the 21st century, Dad!"

"Huh? What do you mean?" asked Dad, looking up from his desk. "I'm a vet, not a brain surgeon."

Zak continued. "Get a new computer – get on the Internet. Times are changing, Dad. You're so totally old-fashioned!"

"Hang on a minute," Dad frowned. "What about that CD player we got last week?"

Zak laughed, "A CD player? Yeah, like that's real

rocket science! And anyway, it was a present from Uncle Martin."

Dad looked defeated. "Well I don't see how the Internet is going to help sort my problems," he muttered.

Then out of nowhere a super-cool-brainwave popped into my head.

COULDN'T YOU START A VET WEBSITE, DAD?

"No way, Betts," he looked amazed. "How could something like that work?"

The cheek of it. "Well, cheers!" I barked. "How about, 'Thanks, Beth, an excellent suggestion. I'll have a think about it.'"

He was looking a bit sheepish now. "Sorry," he sighed, "but my business is going down the drain. I haven't got time to think about computers."

So Dad returned to his writing and that was that. But not for long.

A few days later Zak knocked on my bedroom door.

"That website idea," he said, blinking through his big spectacles. "Of course, Dad could use some of my kit at first. But he'd need at least a one gigahertz processor with an extra 20 gigabytes of hard disk – not to mention 250 megabytes of RAM and that's. . ."

9

"Zak!" I interrupted. "Spit it out. What are you saying?"

"Well, that it's a cool idea," he smiled, "and I think it could work. Let's go for it!"

Most of my friends can't stand their brothers, but with Zak and me it's different. Dad's always busy and now there's just the three of us . . . well, we sort of look after each other. Don't get me wrong, he can be a real pain sometimes, but I wouldn't want anyone else for a brother.

We spent the rest of the day planning: what the website would look like, how it would work and what it would be called. We became more and more excited as things took shape. It had been a brilliant idea and we were starting to believe that it might be the answer to Dad's problems. We'd have to persuade Dad, though. We even made a master plan for that.

Like I said before, I'm the "arty" one in our family, so it was my job to do the drawings. I had to redo some, but once we were both happy, Zak scanned them in. Now we could plan the web pages. Luckily Zak had all the right software. He's such a boffin! The first few designs were disastrous. We soon discovered that you have to keep things simple.

Then at last we got it spot on! Well, we thought so, anyway.

Now it was time for the master plan. Zak pretended to ask Dad for help with his homework.

"What do you think of this, Dad?" he asked, pointing to the computer screen:

DOES YOUR CAT COUGH A LOT?

IS YOUR IGUANA SHY?

DOGGY DILEMMAS?
KITTY CATASTROPHES?
GET ON-LINE AND. . .

 Email your pet problems to me, Doug Kennel, the Internet Vet

 Post messages and photos on the Internet Pet Board

 Advertise your weird and wonderful pet products and remember:

IF YOUR PET'S UPSET CALL THE INTERNET VET!

Dad went quiet. We looked at him. He looked at us, then back at the screen. He smiled.

"Amazing!" he said. "But do you really think it will work? I mean, you know me, I'm hopeless with computers."

"We'll help you." Zak said, "Be positive, Dad. Please. You'll have customers from New York to Newcastle – not just from sleepy little Prestbury."

So that's how it all started. Dad had tons to learn. I think he's always been a bit scared of computers. He did have one cronky old machine, but it was no good for our purposes.

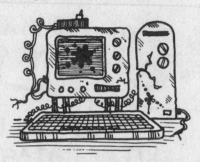

So we had to shift loads of Zak's computer gear into the office by Dad's surgery. Then the lessons began. Zak stayed cool. He tried not to freak Dad out with his usual scientific gobbledegook. To be honest, I learnt quite a bit, too! It wasn't long before Dad was wowed by the whole set up.

"I mean, good grief," he gasped, "I'll be able to send pet advice to Outer Mongolia in seconds!"

We smiled, "Yes Dad, we know."

Of course, Dad didn't get the hang of everything straight away. Any problems he'd had during the day were sorted out after tea and homework.

Things happened slowly at first, but after a few weeks, emails started to trickle in. We'll always remember the very first email. It came from Australia and it wasn't even about a real pet!

From: Billy Bong
Place: Wollongong, Australia
To: The Internet Vet

I'VE SPIED A SPIDER!

G'day Internet Vet

I've just found a furry black spider in my yard. I've always loved spiders and would like to keep him as a pet. Is this OK? He's dead

clever, when I put my hand near him he stands on his back legs! What kind of spider is he? What will he eat?

Cheers mate!
Billy Bong

You should have seen Dad's face. He looked totally gobsmacked.

"Weird," he gasped, "I thought I'd get questions about sick hamsters, not scary spiders!"

He jotted down some titles and asked us to do a bit of research. We settled down in Dad's study and were soon buried in a sea of books. I think he had to buy lots when he was a student. We searched for ages, and then Zak stood up. "This must be it," he said and scurried off to the surgery handing Dad a large book.

"Hmm. An excellent publication," he said, flicking through the pages. "And yes, it's just as I thought." Then putting on a "serious vet" expression, he typed his reply:

Hi Billy

Hey! Don't touch the spider you found, he's deadly.

That's a funnel-web spider in your photo. When you put your hand near him he thinks he's under attack. What will he eat? . . . YOU! He rears up on his hind legs because he's getting ready to bite you with his poisonous fangs.

You'll enjoy the following sensations if he does take a nibble: sweating, muscle twitching, dribbling, vomiting, suffocation, spasms and . . . death.

POISONOUS FANGS ARE DISPLAYED WHEN DANGER THREATENS

Doug Kennel,
Internet Vet

P.S. "Fangs" for the email, let me know how you get on . . . I'd be DEAD interested!

"Cool!" Zak said. "Your first customer, Dad, and you probably saved his life!"

BLUSH!

So things were taking shape. Mind you, we'd have to have a word with Dad about his crummy jokes.

Fart Attack!

The New Year was looking good. Dad was really excited about the Internet Vet project. And from March it really started to take off. Pet lovers from around the world started to check out our website. Companies paid Dad to let them advertise their products. We had a real laugh designing the ads. I sketched the pictures, Dad wrote the copy and Zak did all the boffiny bits.

After school one day, I was helping Dad treat a dog. The poor thing had stumbled while it was running with a stick in its mouth. It was a greyhound. I stroked it as Dad tried to remove a large splinter from its mouth. It would have been enough to drive most pets bonkers, but this sweet hound looked at me with his watery eyes as if to say, "Thanks for helping me."

I didn't know much about these beautiful dogs at the time, but an email from America was to change all that:

From: Jody
Place: Florida, USA
To: The Internet Vet

SKINNY HOUND FOUND!

Hi Internet Vet!

Something happened yesterday and I need your help.

It was Mom who first heard the clattering trashcans and our wailing cat. We rushed outside. Clint was up in the tree hissing at a skinny creature down below. THERE WAS SOME SORT OF DOG SITTING IN OUR YARD! A girl-dog actually. She looked up with her big sad eyes, and limped over to us. CUTE!

She didn't smell too good but I fell in love with her straight away!

That was yesterday. I've given her a bowl of popcorn and some cat food but she still seems sick. She has a damaged leg and keeps making horrible smells. I was gonna call her Cassy, but then I changed it to Gassy because of her farting!

Pop said, "You can't call that stinky dog Gassy!"

"Fine!" I replied, "I'll call her Stinky, instead!"

She's so cute and I wanna keep her! Mom likes her but says she's a racing hound, not a pet. Mom's persuaded Pops to let me look after Stinky for a few days, but no longer. He says there's only room for one pet in our home – and that's his precious Clint. He says he needs a fartin' dog like he needs a hole in his wallet.

Clint

I've snapped some photos to put you in the picture. Can you help? I'd be real grateful!

Me   Stinky   Pop   Mom

Jody

20

P.S. I checked out the local animal shelter and nobody had reported a lost greyhound. They suggested that I pinned some DOG FOUND posters up around our block. I sure hope she isn't claimed!

Yikes. It was a tricky one. Stinky sounded like she needed a vet and we were on the wrong side of the Atlantic Ocean. How could we help?

"That poor hound needs treatment," Dad said. "And if her father is too tight to pay for a vet in the US, Jody will have to take her to an animal shelter."

Zak was staring at the screen, "Stay cool, Dad. Maybe it is a racing greyhound. Can you keep them as pets? Shall we check it out?"

Dad sighed, "Thanks, that would be useful. Let me know what you find out." Then he sat down, tapped out his reply and whizzed it off to the USA.

Hi Jody

It's great that you're able to help this poor dog, even if it is only for a few days. She'll love a bit of food and affection! The sad news is that you might have to take your skinny hound to an animal shelter. I can't persuade your dad to let you keep her. A vet must look at Stinky's leg. This is very important. She also needs to be checked out for worms and fleas. The type of food she's been scavenging probably causes the nasty smells.

Stinky certainly looks like a greyhound but she might be a lurcher (a greyhound crossed with another breed of dog). Take a close look at her ears – you might find something interesting – apart from wax and dead insects, of course.

Keep in touch!

Doug Kennel, Internet Vet

THIS IS A
PUREBRED
GREYHOUND

THIS IS A LURCHER.
HIS DAD IS A
GREYHOUND AND HIS
MUM A LABRADOR

P.S. Has anyone claimed her yet?
P.P.S. Another solution to the smelly problem
. . . stick a peg on your nose!

We spent hours searching through mountains of dog books. There was as much info on farting dogs as racing dogs: "What makes a dog fart?", "How to stop your dog farting" and "Dog farts and human farts – which is worse?" It was yukky but fascinating stuff so we decided to photocopy these bits too. Then flicking through a greyhound magazine (*Fast & Furry*) we found some information about keeping greyhounds as pets.

We handed Dad the information.

"And there's tons of stuff about smelly dogs!" I said. "We're going to compile a 'Fart File'."

Dad looked horrified. "Good grief, is that really necessary?" he asked.

"Yes, it is!" I replied. "We've got a stinky situation on our hands."

"Well, try washing them," he smiled, and disappeared into the surgery, chuckling at his sad joke.

A couple of days later there was an update on the Stinky situation.

From: Jody, Florida, USA
To: The Internet Vet

(HELP!)

Hi Mr Kennel

Good news! I might be allowed to look after Stinky for a little while longer. So far, nobody's called after seeing my posters. Mom says she'll pay the veterinarian's fee if it's not too much. It's a sort of birthday gift for me!

Stinky is staying with the veterinary today while he checks her out. He thinks she has a torn ligament in her leg. I hope she's OK.

The main problem is Pops – he's crazy about our cat, Clint. They sit together watching TV every night. Mom says he pays more attention to the cat than to her. I think Pop reckons Stinky might attack Clint or something. No way! I'm getting to know her now and she just wouldn't do that.

Jody

P.S. Oh yeah! I found letters and numbers tattooed on Stinky's ears. Weird! What do they mean?
P.P.S. You were right about the worms and fleas!
P.P.P.S. She's still farting!

"So she's checked Stinky's ears?" Dad said. "I've jotted some notes down about ear tattoos. Why don't you email them to Jody with some of the other info that you've found?"

THE INTERNET VET

From: Beth (My dad's the Internet Vet)
To: Jody

Hi Jody

It's brilliant that Stinky's leg is being treated. She looks so sweet in the photo! My brother Zak and I have been reading up about greyhounds and Dad's told us about ear tattoos.

He says the tattoos are proof that she *is* a racing greyhound. It might sound weird, but the numbers are a sort of code containing information about Stinky: where she was born, when she was born – all that kind of stuff. We've also found out that loads of greyhounds are abandoned when they get too old, too slow or injured . . . hang on, somebody's just come into Dad's surgery with an injured cat. Dad's trying to hold it but . . . erk! It's peed all down his shirt. Yuk!

Gotta go! Why not post a message on The Internet Pet Board?

Talk soon
Beth

This is a picture we found in one of Dad's magazines

Information about a racing greyhound can be discovered from their ear tattoos

Marvellous! We cleared up the pee while Dad changed into some dry clothes! A car had hit the cat and the driver had brought it in. The driver was as wobbly as the cat she'd run over. So I fixed her up with a cup of tea while Dad looked at the injured mog. We forgot all about Stinky, the tattoo and The Internet Pet Board until later that day.

The Internet Pet Board was another of Zak's brilliant ideas! It's so cool! You just type in your message and in a few seconds, people from all over the world are reading it.

THE INTERNET PET BOARD

TALK TO PET OWNERS AROUND THE WORLD!

Post your message on The Internet Pet Board:
Questions – jokes – photos –
fascinating facts – in fact, anything that
other pet lovers will find interesting.

Message from: Jody, Florida, USA.
Can anybody out there tell me about
greyhounds? I'm trying to persuade my Pop to
let me rescue one!
Thanks

Message from: Mrs Mallard,
Gloucestershire, England.
To: Jody

Hello Jody

I've just read your message!
Ah yes! The greyhound is a
delightful beast. I've had

my hound, Graham for nearly 12 years. Such good company since Mr Mallard passed away. In truth, better company than Mr Mallard when he was alive!

You might like to print this list out and show it to your father!

INTERESTING GREYHOUND FACTS

1. Amazingly, greyhounds don't need much exercise. They're built for short bursts of speed, not long distances. And they never pull on their leads, which is just as well as I'm a bit wobbly on my legs these days.

2. Being gentle, calm and patient, greyhounds make ideal family dogs. Mind you, old people like me find them good company, too.

3. Greyhounds love sleeping on sofas and beanbags. Because they have short hair and no fat to act as padding, their long bony legs need something soft to support them!

4. Greyhounds like eating vegetables! Carrots make an ideal snack. Beware though – I find that too many  greens have the same gassy effect on Graham as they did on Mr Mallard (God rest his soul).

 **5.** Greyhounds love to be warm. Because of their short hair and skinny bodies they really feel the cold. So wrap them up at night!

Yes, Graham's enjoying his retirement. He's finished with the racing life and these days he likes nothing better than to stretch out in front of our roaring log fire.

Hope this helps! Good luck, dear!

Cool! Jody's message had only been on The Internet Pet Board for an hour and she already had some information. I was just about to email her the rest of the greyhound info when I noticed something new on our website.

"Hey, Dad!" I called out. "Have you seen this mad advert?"

In came Dad, a tortoise in one hand, a hamster in the other. He passed them to me and peered down at the screen.

INTERNET VET ADVERTISEMENTS

PURCHASE PET PRODUCTS FROM AROUND THE WORLD!

Ernie's Worm Farm

♥ ATTENTION ALL LIZARD ♥ AND SNAKE KEEPERS! ♥

Take a look at our snack menu

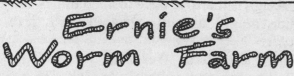

We supply:
juicy mealworms,
red wrigglers, crunchy crickets,
tasty nightcrawlers,
wiggly wax worms and
flavoursome fruit flies

AND GUESS WHAT? Yes, they're all alive!
'Cos that's how your reptiles like 'em,
♥ still a hoppin' and a crawlin'.

♥ And as Ernie says,

Them darn bugs are so fresh I could eat 'em myself... and sometimes I do!

31

"Oh yeah," Dad laughed, "that's Ernie Grubshaw from Colorado, USA. He sent me the copy so I thought I'd have a go at putting an advert together by myself. What d'you think?"

"Hmm, not bad for a beginner. I hope he's joking about eating his bugs, though!" I replied, handing back the rodent and reptile.

"Of course!" Dad laughed. "You know, the thing about design is that you have to keep things simple," he said smugly and disappeared back into his surgery.

I called after him, "Yes Dad, I know." But he wasn't listening and neither was Zak. He had his nose buried in a magazine, as usual. But . . . shock! AMAZEMENT! It wasn't *Computer Geek Weekly*, it was another copy of *Fast & Furry*. These greyhounds were starting to get to him!

Sick and Tired

I suppose I'm a bit nosy (*very* nosy, actually) but I really wanted to know how Jody was getting on with Stinky. I decided that the best way to get an email was to send one! So I tapped out the rest of the greyhound info that we'd dug up and emailed it over.

From: Beth
To: Jody

Hi Jody

Sorry the last message was a bit of a disaster! The weeing cat has been sent home with a plastered leg. How's Stinky's leg? We were wondering what your vet in America had to say about her.

Anyway, if you're interested, here's some more stuff about greyhounds together with some pics that we found:
Greyhound racing seems to be pretty much

like horse racing. The dogs zoom around a track and people gamble money on the one they think will win. The bad news is that greyhounds are sometimes injured in the race. POOR THINGS! If a dog is badly hurt, the owner might decide not to race it again. Even if a dog has managed to escape injury, it will probably have run out of steam by the age of five or six. The trouble is, greyhounds can live for 14 years. That's why there are loads of retired racers looking for homes.

SAVE ME!

PUPPYHOOD

RACING LIFE

RETIREMENT

0 1 2 3 4 5 6 7 8 9 10 11 12 13 14

Y E A R S

THE LIFE OF A RACING GREYHOUND

My boffiny brother, Zak, has been checking out some statistics:

Disgusting bit: more than 20,000 greyhounds are killed every year in the USA when they stop racing.

Good bit: between 10,000 and 15,000 are rescued.

 Another disgusting bit: thousands are killed in Spain, Ireland and the UK, too.

Another good bit: more and more people are finding out what great pets these dogs make.

Looks like Stinky's one of the lucky ones. Maybe she was abandoned after getting hurt. Imagine if we were kicked out of home just because we got sick!

We read Mrs Mallard's message and she's SO right! People need to know what cool pets these dogs can make.

Love to hear how you're getting on. Beth

IT'S TRUE!

After our computer had done the sending bit, an email from Great Uncle Victor in Africa came up on the screen . . . he's dead posh, completely bonkers and a real laugh. . .

From: Uncle Victor, Tanzania, Africa
To: Douglas & family

Douglas, Old Chap!

Surprised but delighted to receive your email.
Thought you didn't like computers! Afraid I
can't be much help on the greyhound front.
However, I've contacted Aunt Agnes in Spain.
Not sure what the Spanish for "greyhound" is
but I've heard the old girl's got a whole pack
of the blighters.
Went greyhound racing years ago at the White
City stadium in London. Terrific fun – you
should take those young people of yours.
Anyway, better get back to work. My research

entitled,
"Toothache in
the African
Honey Badger",
will hopefully
be published
next year.

Regards to
young Zak and
the lovely Beth.

Uncle Victor

Dad was starting to find emails a great way for keeping in touch with our animal-mad relatives. We had uncles and aunts all over the place. And I was finding out how easy it is to make friends through email with someone you've never even met! I was definitely starting to think of Jody as a friend. But, when I next heard from her, the news wasn't good.

From: Jody
To: Beth

Hi Beth

Thought I'd better let you know what's happening. Thanks for the information but I might not need it. Mom and I are sick. It might be something we ate. When we're not vomiting, all we want to do is sleep.

Pop is sort of looking after Stinky, but I'm worried. I mean, he might decide to get rid of her. After all the care I've given her. She was doing so well; the torn ligament in her leg was almost healed.

I'm going bananas thinking I might wake up to find her gone! Pop's always stressed with his work. When he gets home he just crashes in front of the TV with Clint, drinking beer and eating stuff. HE'S SUCH A COUCH POTATO and now he's got to walk my dog. My Pop, WALKING? I don't think so!

Oh and there's more bad news – Pop's started feeding Stinky on really cheap dog food. It might help if Stinky would stop scratching and farting.

Gotta go now, not feeling so good.
See ya

Jody

Not exactly fantastic news. And the scratching and farting seemed the least of her problems. Actually, it wasn't just Stinky with stinky habits. We'd already received quite a few messages asking for help with pongy pets.

From: Davide de Woof,
Brittany, France
To: The Internet Vet

HELP!

MY DOG HAS "DOG BREATH"

Bonjour Internet Vet

My little Fifi has such bad breath! Her teeth look most unpleasant and she won't let me brush them. Is it possible that you can help me?

Merci!
Davide

THE INTERNET VET

Dear Davide

Well, you know what they say about bad breath – IT'S BETTER THAN NO BREATH AT ALL! Still, this doesn't help you much. If the problem is really bad, you will have to visit a vet. He'll be able to scale and polish Fifi's fangs under anaesthetic. This might sound drastic but it will  make a big difference! One easy way to keep Fifi's teeth and gums healthy is to give her plenty of bones and dry dog food to crunch on.

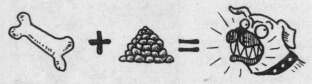

If (like my children) she doesn't like toothbrushes try cleaning her teeth with a piece of cloth. It might sound mad but you'll find different flavoured doggy toothpastes in your pet shop.

Well, there's some info to get your *teeth* into. Mind you, you'll probably want to *chew* it over for a while!

Cheers
Doug Kennel, Internet Vet

Toothpaste for dogs? Yes it's true and we'd just designed an advert for some. . .

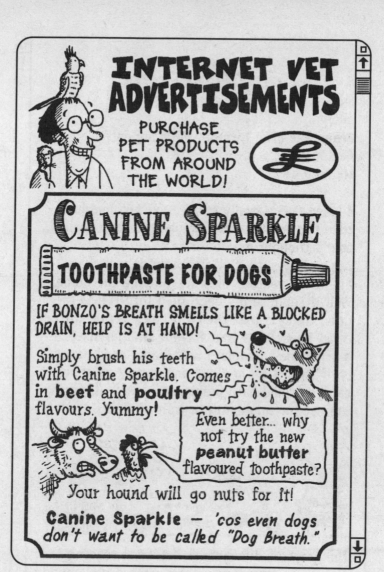

Then Zak did something really annoying. I was *so* hacked off! He sent an email to Jody without telling me. I mean, he didn't even know she was sick.

THE INTERNET VET

From: Zak (The Internet Vet's my dad)

Hi Jody

I know Beth usually emails you but I've just found some important greyhound information that I thought might interest you.
Apparently almost all greyhounds will chase any furry creature they see outside the home. Well, I suppose it's been bred into them. The good thing is that they'll usually get used to other house pets that have a familiar smell – a smell they associate with home and friends. So if Stinky's off her lead and spots a neighbour's cat, you could have problems! As well as hurting the cat she might run in front of a car.

NEIGHBOUR

NEIGHBOUR'S CAT

YOUR CAT IN YOUR HOME

The greyhound magazine I've been reading makes one thing very clear: when a greyhound is chasing something, NOTHING will stop it. It says that you need to find a safe enclosed area for your hound to run in.

I also read a story about a bloke who lived by the sea with his greyhound. He walked his dog along the cliff tops every day. One morning his greyhound spotted a rabbit and ran after it. The rabbit disappeared down a hole on the cliff edge but the chasing greyhound couldn't stop and ran right over the cliff. Apparently, this happens to quite a few dogs every year. What a way to go! I guess it shows that you have to think very carefully before letting a greyhound off its lead.

Gotta go now. I'm fitting a couple of 32-megabyte chips in this computer to pump up the RAM.

Zak

"You're fitting a couple of 32-megabyte chips to pump up the RAM?" I asked him. "What planet are you on? Don't you know she's ill and worried that her slobby Dad might chuck Stinky out? You're such a dope, sometimes."

"Well pardon me for trying to help!" he snapped. "S'pose I'd better crawl back to my room and finish the Fart File. Or do you want to take that over, too?"

Yes, well. I was only thinking of my friend. Bet the last thing she wanted to hear was that Stinky might take a bite out of the neighbour's cat and then cause a traffic accident.

Cat in a Flap

A few days later, I was busy helping Dad in the surgery.

"Take a look at this iguana," Dad said. "She's called Lizzy. Notice anything about her?"

"Er, that she's freaky looking and gives me the creeps?" I replied, keeping a healthy distance from the rather large lizard.

"Yes, that's very helpful," Dad sighed. "What about her legs?"

I stepped forward nervously and peered down at the creature.

"Well," I paused. "They look a bit wonky I suppose."

"I'd say they were deformed rather than wonky," Dad laughed. "But you're right."

"So what made them wonky, er, deformed?" I asked.

"Aha," said Dad, only too pleased to be able to show off a bit of knowledge, "it's all down to a lack of light! Not just any old light, either. Iguanas need UVB light to help their bones grow properly."

"So what is UVB light, as if you weren't going to tell me?"

Dad got serious, "Well, lots of different types of light rays combine to make sunlight. UVB rays are in sunlight and they help iguanas and other reptiles to make a special vitamin."

"Sounds complicated!" I said, then realized I was in for an even more in-depth explanation.

"Yes, it does, but it's amazing, too. You see, this vitamin helps the iguana's guts to get calcium from the food that it eats. If reptiles don't get enough calcium, their bones don't grow properly and they become deformed."

"Like Lizzy!" I chipped in. Dad's ramblings were actually making sense for once. "Iguanas come from South America, don't they? Lizzy would have got much more sunlight there than she gets here."

"Spot on!" said Dad, and he grinned at me. "Over here she's been hiding behind rocks because she felt ill. Her owner thought she was just being shy, but lots of animals like to find a quiet, dark place when they feel sick."

"So what's the diagnosis, Doc?" I asked, managing to give Lizzy's scales a little tickle.

"Well, the owner will have to get a UVB lamp to

put in Lizzy's tank. Lizards and snakes need a lot of care. People often don't realize this. I mean, Lizzy could grow up to two metres long. That's bigger than me crawling around on all fours!"

"Gruesome," I said. "They must eat a lot, then?"

"Yes, but not meat," Dad was in full flow. "It's all fruit and veg, except Brussels sprouts, they're bad for iguanas. A healthy creature will be bright green. He'll eat every day and he'll poo every day."

"Delightful," I grimaced. "Give me a greyhound any time."

"Greyhounds, that reminds me!" exclaimed Dad. "I keep forgetting to tell you and Zak that we're all going racing on Easter Saturday. A sort of holiday treat."

My first reaction was, "Wow, fantastic!" But then I remembered the email we'd sent to Jody.

"I hope there won't be any injuries," I said.

"Think of it as research," Dad replied. "We'll go and make our own minds up about greyhound racing."

Zak wasn't keen when I told him about our trip to the track. "We shouldn't be supporting a sport like that," he said crossly.

But when I told him about it being research, he thought again.

"Yeah, OK, we'll treat it as a fact-finding mission," he said reluctantly. "I suppose the info will be useful for my new project."

"What new project?" I asked.

"Well, the Fart File web pages are almost sorted," he said, "so I thought I'd do a Greyhound File for our website after that. You can help if you like. It'll be a cool way of encouraging people to keep greyhounds."

A fcw days later we had another update on the Stinky situation.

From: Jody
To: Beth

Hi guys!

How's it going? Things are getting back to normal (whatever normal is) here.

Mom and me are feeling a whole lot better and Pop hasn't chucked Stinky out. Yet. Even Clint seems to have gotten used to having Stinky around the place. Mind you, I don't think he likes her foul farts any more than we do.

Hey, guess what happened the other evening? Pop's TV was way too loud as usual. I stuck my head round

the door to ask him to turn it down. I swear,
POP WAS STROKING THE DOG. His hand shot
away from Stinky when he heard me and
grabbed his can of beer.

"You should be in bed, little lady," he
grumbled. "Stick this hound in the back room,
first. Then get yourself back upstairs!"

He was looking a little pink in the face. I
couldn't help smiling. And where was Clint? I
mean, he always, ALWAYS curls up on Pop's lap
when the TV's on.

Then yesterday Mom asked me where I'd got
the bone from.

"What bone?" I asked.

"The bone that Stinky's chewing," she replied. "I didn't give it to her so I guessed you must have."

Well I didn't. So it must have been. . . POP!

Mom warned me, "Now don't go teasing him, honey. You gotta let him make friends with that dog in his own way. You know what he's like."

So that's my latest. What's been happenin' with you guys?

See ya
Jody

Stinky and the Couch Potato – it was a gripping story! Was he really developing a soft spot for the farting hound? Time would tell. Meanwhile, The Internet Pet Board was chock full of pet stuff from around the world. There seemed to be a "Stinky Theme" developing here, too:

THE INTERNET PET BOARD

TALK TO PET OWNERS AROUND THE WORLD!

Post your message on The Internet Pet Board:
Questions – jokes – photos –
fascinating facts – in fact, anything that
other pet lovers will find interesting.

Lee Pong, Beijing, China
Can anybody out there tell me why my Pekingese dog smells so bad? I'd never get rid of him, not for all the tea in China, but what can I do?

Hans Zoff, Hamburg, Germany
Hi there Pong. It's not your dog's fault that he smells so doggy – he is a dog, after all! Longhaired breeds tend to pong more than shorthaired ones. Worth remembering if you're thinking of getting a dog.

Shorthaired hounds are also easier to keep clean. Mud doesn't have so much hair to cling to. And if they get wet, shorthaired mutts dry off much quicker than hairy hounds. That's why I always have whippets and greyhounds. They're such clean dogs.

What do you do if your dog whiffs? Give him a bath. Like us, they need a scrub every now and then. Make sure you use dog shampoo, though. Mum's shampoo irritated my dog's skin when I tried it. (And Mum found it irritating that I'd used her shampoo!)

If your pet REALLY STINKS you may need the vet to look him over. It could be more than a bath that's called for. There's a really smelly skin condition called seborrhoea. It smells disgusting, like rotten fish mixed with mouldy sick. What's more, it causes the skin to

flake. This problem is pretty unusual though. So it's true, all dogs smell – some a lot more than others!

Wendy Miller, Auckland, New Zealand

SORRY TO KICK UP A STINK BUT. . . It's not my dog that's the problem, it's Whiffo, my son's ferret. He has a ghastly smell and I don't think I can stand it much longer. If nothing can be done I'm afraid Whiffo will have to go. Can anyone help?

Simon Weasley-Warner, Surrey, England
Message to Wendy Miller.
All ferrets pong, old thing, they have scent glands at the base of their tail. In the wild,

the stinky smell from the glands is used to scare off enemies and also to mark territory.

STINKY SCENT GLAND

I've got 18 ferrets and it's just the way they are. So there's nothing wrong with young Whiffo. You can bath the poor little chap every day for the rest of his life, he'll still smell.

One bit of good news – some vets can do a special operation to remove the scent gland from a ferret. Don't turn your nose up at this . . . it might be worth looking into!

Mrs Mallard, Gloucestershire, England
To: Jody and other greyhound lovers

Hello Dear
I do hope your father allowed you to rescue a greyhound. I've written a few more snippets of information that might help to win him over:

INTERESTING GREYHOUND FACTS part two

1. Greyhounds are intelligent and sensitive (rather like me). Adopting a racing greyhound means that you're getting a dog that's been trained in many things already. Your main task will be to teach them what it's like to live in a house rather than a kennel. One thing I've learnt is that because of their sensitivity they respond better to kindness than fear.

WRONG!

RIGHT!

2. When training a dog, you have to remember that they think they live in a pack. This pack is actually your family and the owner of the dog has to show that he or she is the leader!

WRONG!

RIGHT!

It sounds crazy, but some people control their dogs by growling at them. In dog language this means, "I'm in charge!"

I think training a dog is like training a husband – you only need a few simple commands like, "WAIT!", "THIS WAY!" and "SIT!"

Mind you, greyhounds don't like sitting, they seem to find it uncomfortable and prefer to lie down.

3. Greyhounds love listening to music – it's often played in the racing kennels. Like many greyhounds, my Graham finds classical music more soothing than heavy rock. So if you pop out and leave your greyhound on his own, stick the radio on for him!

GRAHAM LISTENING TO HIS FAVOURITE COMPOSER – J.S. BARK... I MEAN, J.S. BACH!

4. Greyhounds love to ride in cars! They're driven to the racetrack from an early age.

My Graham has never once been sick in the car. (Unlike Mr Mallard – God rest his soul.)

Of course, riding in cars, listening to music and walking nicely on a lead, are all habits picked up in racing kennels. A greyhound raised at home from a puppy might behave quite differently!
Good luck and goodbye, dear!

Mrs Mallard

Our visit to the greyhound racetrack on Easter Saturday was brilliant fun. Most race meetings are in the evening so it was quite late when we got back. Dad wanted me to go to bed.

"What's the point of holidays if you can't stay up for a bit?" I argued. "Anyway, I want to email Jody. She'll be dead interested to hear about our evening. Pleeeeease, Dad. I'll make you a hot chocolate while you watch the footy."

"What about *me*?" Zak sounded put out.

"OK, OK, I'll make you both one and you can have a bit of my Easter egg if you'll just let me get on with it."

Dad was already disappearing into the living room "Oh, go on then," he sighed.

"Yes!" I clenched my fist and skipped into the office.

From: Beth

Hi Jody
Guess where we've just been? Greyhound racing! We wanted to find out for ourselves what it's all about. Dad took us as an Easter holiday treat. It's been a freezing night and very busy with a race every 15 minutes. Still, I must admit we had quite a laugh.

We got chatting to a woman called Mrs Betts who owned one of the dogs that raced this evening and she told us all about greyhound racing. She said that it's no good just being a fast greyhound. The best racers learn to save some of their energy for later in the race.

Dogs that shoot out from the traps and burn up all their energy too quickly will never win a race. They also have to be quite clever, keeping one eye on the thing they're chasing, and one eye on all the other dogs around them. One false move can cause a

pile-up. The poor things often suffer broken bones, pulled tendons, torn ligaments (like Stinky has) and dislocated toes. Ouch!

Did you know that females are just as fast as males? And what's more, the dogs are tested for drugs that might help them to run faster – just like human athletes!

Before each race, people in white coats walked the six dogs around the track. This was so we could take a look at them before placing a bet. The dogs were patted and stroked as they walked round and seemed quite happy.

There were TV screens everywhere giving race information. We each chose a dog and Dad put a bet on for us (just a quid). I chose number one, Freddy's Rocket. Zak chose number five, Slippery Loo, and Dad chose number six, Clever Wally.

The dogs were put into traps – a sort of little cage with a door that sprang open when the races started. Each trap had its own colour.

The dogs looked cool in their trendy coloured coats. Number one was red, two was blue, three was white, four was black, five was orange and six had black and white stripes.

Of course, on the track they didn't chase cats, or any sort of live animal. Instead there was a sort of mechanical rabbit, like a toy, really, that started off on the other side of the track from the traps.

The dogs got really excited. There was lots of whining and yapping just before the rabbit reached the traps. As it whizzed past, the doors snapped open and the greyhounds shot out after it. They were SO fast!

The coloured coats made it easy to keep track of the hounds as they whizzed round. Almost immediately, Freddy's Rocket went into the lead. Then Zak's Slippery Loo started to catch up. Dad's Clever Wally was in last place all the way round! The other three (black, white and blue coats) were closing in on our two. Twenty yards to go, and Freddy was still leading with Slippery Loo catching up. Could he hold on? We were jumping up and down going completely bonkers as they shot past the finishing line. Who'd won? The race was so close that it had to be decided by a slow motion video.

Shivering with excitement (and cold!) we stared up at the screen. First. . . Slippery Loo.

WIN - SLIPPERY LOO

 Zak was punching the air and making stupid whooping noises – very childish. Still, my dog came second, which was better than Dad's Clever Wally. Zak was still grinning like an idiot when Dad handed him his winnings!

Zak and I chatted about greyhound racing on the way home. We both agreed the actual racing didn't seem cruel. I mean, greyhounds are ace speed machines. They're born to run and they seem to enjoy it! Mrs Betts obviously loved her greyhounds and told us that she had six retired racers at home. The cruel bit is what happens when they get too old and slow to win races. If they could all find cosy homes like Stinky has, there wouldn't be a problem.

Anyway, it's brilliant news about your Dad. He'll be taking Stinky for "walkies" next! It's late, so I'd better go.

Write soon,
Love Beth

I could hear *Match of the Day* still going in the other room as I sent the email off. I could see that Dad and Zak's faces were fixed on the TV screen. They didn't seem too bothered about their drinks. I tiptoed back to the computer. Time to check out some of the emails Dad had been replying to:

From: Heidi Seek, Switzerland
To: The Internet Vet

TUBBY OR NOT TUBBY?

Hello Internet Vet

There's so much talk about couch potato people these days. Well, I've got a couch potato dog!

We all sit watching TV in the evening eating crisps and chocolates. It seems mean not to give some to Bigbelly, our Basset hound. He just sits there looking hopeful and we always give in. He loves the TV and loves eating snacks but his stomach is almost touching the floor! He's always shared our grub, I don't think he'll understand if we stop feeding him.

Help!
Heidi

THE INTERNET VET

Heidi Hi, I mean, Hi Heidi

Things have got to change – you've been killing Bigbelly with kindness! Fatty, salty foods are bad for dogs and Bigbelly could end up with arthritis and heart disease.

Firstly, get him checked out by your vet to make sure he doesn't have a medical problem. He'll also be able to tell you exactly what food this dog should be eating. Try giving him three small meals a day instead of one big one and gradually reduce the quantities. Give him healthy titbits, maybe a carrot or an apple core, and cut out all the other stuff. A healthy walk is better than an unhealthy snack. Go for it! – he'll be much happier and so will you!

Happy slimming!
Doug Kennel, Internet Vet

I was just about to turn the computer off when another email came through. Wow, that was quick. It was from Jody. What was she doing at this time of night? Then I remembered. Durrrr! It was early evening in Florida!

From: Jody

Hi Beth

Just got your message. Thought I'd get back to you straight away. Thanks for telling me about the racing. I'm real glad I found Stinky before anything horrible could happen to her.

Anyhow, you will not believe what Pop's done now. He's been trying to find out about Stinky's past. Crazy! Not long ago he didn't want anything to do with her. Now he wants to know all about her. He phoned the National Greyhound Association guys and asked for her ear tattoo code.

They've promised to send us her details. I think Pop wants to know if Stinky won any races. I guess it would be interesting. I just hope he's not up to anything.

The other thing is that Clint has gone. We haven't seen him since yesterday morning. I sure hope he turns up soon. Pop thinks Stinky scared him off. No way! Clint was

getting used to her.
If he was gonna
leave home he'd
have done it way
back.

See ya
Jody

Odd. It had sounded like they were all getting on quite well. When I told Dad about Jody's email he gave me some advice to pass on to her. I was hoping that maybe Clint had already turned up. Still, I tapped the message out anyway:

From: Beth

Hi Jody

Really sorry to hear about Clint. I know how much your Pop loves him. Maybe he'll have turned up by the time you read this.

Dad asked if he was "chipped"? A vet can scan a lost pet to see if it's got a computer chip under its skin. The chip will give details of the owner.

I suppose cat collars are a cheaper solution. Dad says the best collars are elasticated. If they get caught on a branch, the elastic stretches and the cat can escape. Collars with bells are good, they warn birds and mice that there's a cat on the prowl!

ELASTIC
BELL

BLAST!

TING-A-LING!

I guess Clint could have been away for a few days now but try not to worry. There are lots of true stories about cats that have turned up after disappearing for months. Some had been stolen or had climbed into lorries but they managed to travel hundreds of miles to find their way home!

HMMM, COMFY SOFA

MOVE NOW

You're lucky Clint's a cat, though! Dad told me about this tortoise that escaped from his cage in 1960. A neighbour found him 35 years later and he'd only travelled 750 yards!

I hope that made you laugh!

I'm sure Clint will turn up and when he does, make a fuss of him. That's what we did with our cat Archie. He disappeared for days. Then he strolled in through his cat-flap like he'd never been away.

We'd been so worried. Why had he gone off? Anyway, I stuffed him full of tuna just to remind him that home isn't such a bad place after all!

One other thing that Dad suggests. If you ever get a knucklebone for Stinky, buy an extra one for Clint. It will stop any jealousy (that might have made him run off in the first place) and gnawing on bones is good for their teeth too!

I know this might not help 'cos he's probably still missing but let me know what happens.

Beth

P.S. Dad's just popped his head round the door with another bit of advice. He says, "Never give chicken bones to a cat or dog. They splinter and cause choking." Fascinating!

P.P.S. Have you seen the ad we did for Pet Chips?

INTERNET VET ADVERTISEMENTS

PURCHASE PET PRODUCTS FROM AROUND THE WORLD!

IT'S CHIPS WITH EVERYTHING THESE DAYS!

Micro chips, wood chips, oven chips, pet chips... Yes, that's right - PET CHIPS! But they're not doggy dinners. These teeny microchips hold important information. If Pusskins or Rover go missing, your details are stored on the chip. Pass a scanner over a chipped pet and the details come up on screen.

MICROCHIP IS HIDDEN UNDER PET'S SKIN

Name: Dennis
Tel: 29876547
Address:
14 Claws lane
Mogshire

So many cats and dogs end up in animal shelters with no identity...
DON'T LET THIS HAPPEN TO YOUR PET!

We had two weeks holiday ahead and not much homework. Zak had almost finished the Fart File and it looked brill. I should have been feeling happy but I'd been moping round the house all day. Then Dad called out from the study. "Hey Betts, do you remember that wacky Australian, Billy Bong? Well, he's up to his tricks again. Come and take a look."

From: Billy Bong
Place: Wollongong, Australia
To: The Internet Vet

G'day mate

Thanks for the spider info. My dad put him back out in the outback where he belonged. It was a shame 'cos I really wanted an unusual pet. Things are looking up though – my mate Wacker has just given me one of his frogs. It's a beaut, though I'm not sure why he didn't want the colourful little fella!

Can you tell me more about him?
Cheers
Billy

"He's barmy," Dad laughed. "Still, we'd better help out. Fancy a bit of research?"

So it was back to the study. Zak helped too but it was me who discovered what sort of frog Billy had. Double-checking, I looked at Billy's photo again. Then I looked at the photo in Dad's book. I moved my face in close to make sure I wasn't mistaken. I wasn't.

"DAD!" I screamed, and ran into the surgery. Dad was holding a Siamese cat. I'm pretty sure it was about to scratch him anyway. Still, I don't suppose my screaming helped.

"Crikey, what's happened?" Dad asked, shaking his bleeding hand furiously.

"The frog, Dad. It's deadly. You've got to email Billy at once."

Dad checked the frog info I'd found. Two minutes later his bandaged finger was tapping out a reply to Australia.

THE INTERNET VET

Hi Billy

DON'T TOUCH THE FROG!

He's got enough deadly poison on him to kill 2,000 humans! He's called a Poison Arrow Frog. Natives in the South American jungle dip their arrows in the poison. Any creature they shoot dies instantly and so will you if you stroke him!

Keep him in the glass container and take him to a pet shop that knows about reptiles and amphibians.

DO IT NOW!

Doug Kennel, Internet Vet

P.S. Where the heck did Wacker get the frog? South America's a long way from Australia!
P.P.S. Couldn't you just have a hamster or something?

The frog incident took my mind off Clint and Stinky for a while even if it didn't exactly cheer me up.

"Billy would be better off with a greyhound," Zak said. "I think they have greyhound racing in Australia. I'll tell him to look at our Greyhound File when it's up and running."

"Have we got enough space on our site for that?" Dad asked.

Zak was looking smug. "Oh yes," he said, "I've re-sized all the gifs which has given us loads more space on the server. It'll speed up our download time, too."

"Good grief!" Dad muttered, disappearing back into the surgery, "I wish I'd never asked."

The Rotten Couch Potato

"Ouch! See if you can find some gloves in that cupboard, Betts," Dad yelped, putting the hedgehog back on the table. He didn't often deal with wild animals but a young girl had brought it in. She'd looked so worried that we'd promised to check the creature out for her. I passed Dad some gardening gloves.

"Well, there doesn't seem to be anything wrong with the little chap," Dad said, "except that it's March and he should be hibernating. Perhaps a cat disturbed him. Give the Hedgehog Hospital a call. They'll probably look after him till Spring comes."

The hedgehog was so cute. "Shall I give him a bit of bread and milk?" I asked.

"Bread and milk is too rich for hedgehogs, meat-based dog or cat food's best," said Dad, sounding like a human textbook. "Then give him a saucer of water. After that you can stick Spike in a box lined with hay."

"Spike? Oh yes, very amusing," I gave a weak laugh. "Can you keep hedgehogs as pets?"

Dad sounded firm. "No, they're wild animals," he insisted. "You can encourage them to live in your garden, though."

"What, leave food out for them?" I asked.

"Yes, when the weather gets cold. And you can leave part of the garden wild for hedgehogs to live in, as long as you never use slug pellets and always check bonfires before lighting them. That's just the sort of place they might crawl into for a nap."

Zak dashed in just as the hedgehog lesson ended.

"Right I've finished formatting the web files and I've uploaded the HTML pages. We're in business," he jabbered enthusiastically.

"You what?" I asked.

Dad looked even more puzzled than me. "Look, I know it's boring for you but could we have that in Earth language?" he groaned.

"The Fart File – it's up and running!" Zak announced.

We shuffled into the office. "Cool, let's take a look," I said.

"Hang about, there was an email from Jody, too," Zak said and added with heavy sarcasm, "don't worry, I haven't read it. Thought I'd better get your permission first."

"Yes, ha ha," I snapped. "Come on, let's find out what's happening in Florida."

From: Jody

Hi Beth

Disaster! I just can't believe it. Pop was really starting to bond with Stinky.

The tattoo information's come through and Pop's determined to track down Stinky's owner. I still don't know if it's because of the farting or Clint disappearing.

There was kind of a catastrophe last evening when Pop's boss and his wife came for supper. I don't think the smell of Stinky's farts made a good impression – they left early.

And where is Clint? I've put LOST CAT posters up everywhere and we keep checking at the animal shelter. I know Pop misses him and so do I. Now it looks like I might lose Stinky, too!

Help!
Jody

We stared at the screen. "Her rotten couch potato dad!" I wailed. "After all she's done for Stinky. How could he?"

"Steady, Betts," Dad said, "he might be doing the right thing. I mean, they don't know Stinky was abandoned. Maybe the owner's been looking for her, she. . ."

"Get real, Dad," Zak butted in. "She must have been chucked out. What about her bad leg?"

"Zak's right," I backed him up. "I reckon Couch Potato couldn't stand the farting any more. Jody should have tried harder to sort it out."

"OK, OK," Dad put his hands up. "Well what about this, er, Smelly File thing you've been doing? Perhaps Jody might find some useful information there. In fact, somebody emailed me yesterday with a similar problem."

From: Erik de Plop, Holland
To: The Internet Vet

HELP! MY DOG CAN'T STOP FARTING

Hi Internet Vet!

It's true, he watches telly with us after his daily meal and produces really ghastly guffs!

He has a healthy diet – a big bowl of meat with lots of green veg. When it first started happening we thought it was Dad, but the pongs are just as bad when he's not there. Well, they're different, anyway!

DAD

What can be dung, I mean, done?
Erik

It seemed that people all around the world were having problems with their farting dogs. We decided to tell Jody about the Fart File straight away:

THE INTERNET VET

From: Beth

Hi Jody

That's really bad news. Quick! Take a look at the Fart File on our website. It offers loads of help for farting dogs. If you get it sorted fast, maybe your dad will change his mind.

Beth

What more could we do? Would the Fart File save the situation?

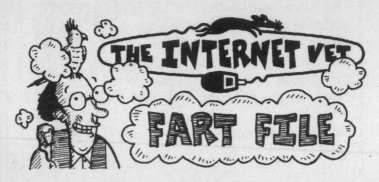

THE INTERNET VET
FART FILE

Does your dog keep "letting off?"
Is life a real "gas" in your household?

Well, read on. . .

AIR TRAPPED IN DOG'S TUMMY

AIR → AIR

Where do farts come from?
Most farts come from swallowed air but they also come from gas made by bacteria living in your dog's guts. Sounds horrible? Well, you've got fart-making bacteria in your guts, too!

Why are dog farts different from human farts?
This is due to the different foods that we eat and also because we have different bacteria in our guts. Mind you, you could try eating dog food for a week and then compare your farts with Fido's!

What makes farts smell?
The smelliest ingredient in all farts is a gas called hydrogen sulphide.

Is it just dogs and humans that fart?
No. All animals fart!

Which smell worse – dog farts or human farts?

FARTOLOGIST

This is a tricky one, but most fartologists (if there is such a scientist) would agree that dog farts are the worst. Dog diets are high in proteins (from the meat that they eat) and proteins contain lots of the sulphur that's found in hydrogen sulphide. Humans produce more farts

NO PROBLEM!

but they're usually less smelly. Large plant eaters, such as cows, horses and elephants produce gigantic farts that hardly smell at all!

Snake and turtle farts are especially pongy, although there's no scientific evidence to prove it! Scientists think that fish probably fart, too, especially coral-eating fish (coral contains gas-producing chemicals). Jellyfish, on the other hand, have different intestines from most other animals and couldn't fart, even if they wanted to!

Dog farts and human farts – which are louder?

Some scientists say that because humans are embarrassed about farting, they desperately try to keep them in. So when a human fart does manage to escape, it blasts out with a loud raspberry sound. Dogs, on the other hand, couldn't care less who hears them fart and this relaxed attitude, scientists claim, allows a doggy fart to drift out silently.

What starts doggy farts?

1. CAUSE – Gulping food down too quickly is the most common cause. Your dog will be gulping air as well as food. The air builds up in the intestines and turns into fart gas. How does it escape? Through his bottom!

REMEDY – To stop your dog gulping, try putting a couple of tennis balls or rocks in his food. He'll be forced to eat round the objects and this will slow his eating down. Another way to help stop your dog gulping is to raise

his feeding bowl up about 25 centimetres. An upside-down plastic bowl or cardboard box is ideal for this.

2. CAUSE – A rescued dog can be stressed by re-homing and this can often cause farting. This stress together with a change in diet can be the cause of constant fart attacks.

REMEDY – Once a rescued dog settles down in his new home, he will no longer be so stressed. Once you've found a food that agrees with your dog, try to stick with it.

3. CAUSE – Rich treats and green vegetables. Too much of these and you'll be in for a treat . . . a smelly one!

REMEDY – Cut down on green vegetables, carrots are better. Make sure that the treats you give your dog are not too rich. A raw-hide chew is a fart-free treat and will be enjoyed just as much as a tin of oily, fart-making fish.

4. CAUSE – Food scavenged from bins or on a walk.

MOULDY BURGERS   DEAD RABBITS   COWPATS

REMEDY – Dogs love to scavenge but don't let them eat things that they find on walks. Rotting carcasses can cause stomach upsets. This is likely to involve a fart-attack followed closely by a bout of diarrhoea. Nice!

5. CAUSE – Intestinal parasites (worms). It'll take guts to sort these out.

REMEDY – De-worm your dog regularly. Pills can be bought from the vet and as well as helping to stop the farting it will ensure the general health of your dog. It can be tricky to

get some dogs to swallow a pill. Once it's in the dog's mouth, tickle his throat and he'll swallow whether he wants to or not! You can also be sneaky and hide pills in dog food or little lumps of cheese!

6. CAUSE – Cheap dog foods containing fillers and by-products. Yuk, these are simply offal, I mean, awful.

REMEDY – Feed your dog with good quality food. The products used to fill out cheap dog foods often cause farting. Also, as cheap food contains less goodness, your dog will need more of it.

One last tip. Take your dog for a walk after his dinner. This will help his digestion so he'll fart a lot less!

As a last resort there are medicines available for farting dogs. . .

So now you know just about everything there is to know about farting!

Good luck and remember,
STOP THE FOG THAT SEEPS FROM YOUR DOG!

Dad was still staring at the screen. "Good grief, you haven't left much out!" he gasped.

"Maybe I should have checked it all first."

Zak was looking smug. "Good, though, isn't it?" he boasted. "I reckon Jody should try the whole lot."

Keen to escape the subject of farting dogs, Dad opened a drawer in his desk. "Do you remember Uncle Victor talking about Aunt Agnes and her dogs?" he asked.

"Oh yeah," Zak replied. "She was supposed to email us some stuff about greyhounds."

"Oh please!" I moaned, "I'm getting a headache just thinking about them. I'm going up to my room."

Dad was waving a piece of paper. "Hang on," he said, "Aunt Agnes sent a really interesting letter. Go on, have a read. It's hilarious."

Dad's idea of something being hilarious seemed to make it even less appealing. Still, we had a read. I didn't exactly split my sides laughing but I've got to admit it was pretty interesting. . .

Cordoba, Spain

Dougy Darling!

I hear from old
Vic that you're
interested in
greyhounds. Blasted PC's up the
spout so I've penned a letter
instead.

   I have to admit, of all the mutts
I've had, greyhounds are my
favourite. I've got 12 at the
moment - all of them "galgos"; this is
what Spanish greyhounds are called.
These days I spend most of my time
rescuing the poor beggars.

   I'd say I know pretty much
everything there is to know about
these darling dogs, so I thought I'd
pass on to you some of the tastier
titbits. Can there be another family
of dog with such a fascinating
history?

FOR A START, THEY'VE BEEN MODELS FOR SOME ANCIENT WORKS OF ART!

I bet you didn't know about the cave in Turkey, with walls decorated with hunting scenes? Which dogs did they take hunting? Well, with their long bodies and long thin legs, they're certainly greyhound-type dogs. The paintings date back something like 8,000 years (they're even older than Vic!).

GREYHOUNDS CREEP INTO LEGENDS TOO

Ever heard of the poet Homer? He lived in Ancient Greece in around 800 BC! He wrote about the travels of Odysseus. Odysseus was away from home for 20 years! Who was it that recognized him when he first got back? You guessed it, his faithful old greyhound, Argos.

GREYHOUNDS HAVE RUBBED SHOULDERS WITH ROYALTY

Ancient Egyptian Pharoah, Tutankhamun kept greyhounds. They had a marvellous life, treated better than children or slaves - except when King Tut died, his hounds went with him. They were buried in Tut's tomb, so they could follow him into the next world. Bet they were pleased!

THE KING'S DEAD!

King Knut and William the Conqueror both had royal greyhounds. In fact, if you'd been around in the 10th century, when they ruled, you wouldn't have been allowed to keep a greyhound. They were strictly for

CHOP! HOWL!

kings. William the Cong even ordered the toes to be chopped off rival dogs, so that his greyhounds were always fastest! Now that was definitely taking things too far.

King Henry VIII had even more greyhounds than he had wives! (I dare say the dogs got better treatment, too!)

FANCY A CHOP?

Even miserable old Queen Victoria had an Italian greyhound called EOS. She had a portrait painted with EOS in her arms. Aaaah!

THEY'VE EVEN BEEN OFF EXPLORING!

Christopher Columbus was asked to take 20 greyhounds on his second trip to America in 1493. At first he wasn't keen but then some bright spark suggested that the hounds could be used to try out new foods. If the dogs weren't poisoned, the food was fit for humans! Charming!

TRY THIS, BOY!

PHWOAR!

BOY CAN THEY RUN

Greyhounds were obviously the best hunting dogs around for centuries.

In the end, a sport called coursing took over from

hunting. This is a competition where the greyhounds chase after hares and it was really popular in the 18th and 19th centuries (except with the hares). Eventually, someone had the bright idea of using some sort of pretend hare, and greyhound racing was born!

PHEW!

It's a tragedy what's happening to these dogs today, it was their hunting skills that earned them a right royal treatment in the past. But today, because their racing life is so short, they often don't get anything like the respect they

deserve - some even
end up in scientific
research labs.

So, it's hurrah
for people like me,
who set up comfy retirement homes
for needy ex-racers. And for the
rescue organizations that are
starting to pop up all over the place.
Three cheers for us all! Hip, hip, etc.

Love to all
Aunt Agnes

P.S. Vic's been telling me about your
website. I hear you've got a whole
section on farting. Hope he's read it
carefully - poor
blighter's always
had probs in that
department!

Dad was still chuckling to himself. "She's a scream!
Isn't she?"

"Yes, Dad," we replied dutifully.

In the Doghouse

I was holding a miserable-looking rabbit for Dad. The tubes between its eyes and nose were blocked which made it look like it was crying.

"Still worrying about Jody?" Dad asked, squirting some liquid into the rabbit's weepy eyes. "I don't know who looks more fed up. You or the rabbit," he chuckled.

"It's not funny Dad," I sulked. "I know it might seem mad to you, but I think of Jody as my friend. It was brilliant when she first rescued Stinky. I think we really helped her and now it's all going wrong."

"Things will work out," he reassured me.

That's what he thought.

From: Jody
To: Beth

STINKY'S GONE!

I followed the Fart File advice and it worked! I cut down on the green stuff and rich foods, raised up her bowl, wormed her and only fed

FART FREE

her good quality food. It only took a few days and the farting had stopped! But it still wasn't enough to change Pop's mind.

He tracked down the kennel where Stinky had grown up and the three of us set off to find it. What a miserable journey. I just sat in the back of the station wagon hugging my dog.

Mr Leech, the kennel boss, told us that Honey Dancer (Stinky's real name) had been bought by a Mrs Crook. Mrs Crook buys injured greyhounds and tries to get them fit for racing again. He reckoned Stinky must have escaped and thanked us for bringing her back.

There was something a bit creepy about Mr Leech. He had a sneering sort of smile on his face as he checked Stinky over.

Honey Dancer (I don't think he liked the name we'd given her) would never race again, he told us, and Mrs Crook wouldn't want her back. Then the smile reappeared, he asked us not to worry – he'd give the hound a happy retirement. Mr Leech seemed amazingly cheerful to discover that Honey Dancer wouldn't be returning to the track. To be honest, I didn't like him. Pop didn't seem to notice any of this. I reckon he'd made his mind up before we'd even set out that day. Stinky was going back to the kennels and that was that. Pop even admitted that he liked the dog. But he said that Clint obviously didn't, otherwise why else would he have run off? He said if the two animals had gotten on, it might have been different. I pleaded with

Pop to change his mind, but he wouldn't budge.

So farting hadn't been the main problem, after all. Pop missed his cat and he blamed Stinky for Clint disappearing. It's just SO unfair, Beth. I mean, Pop may have loved his cat but he'd grown fond of Stinky, too. Now we're back home and I know Pop's missing both of them.

I can't stop thinking about Stinky sitting there in the kennels on her own.

Sorry. I don't feel much like writing any more right now.

Thanks for your help, Beth.

"Maybe Jody could get a different type of dog," said Zak, being annoyingly cheerful. "Maybe not a greyhound, but there's loads of other greyhound-type breeds."

"You don't get it, do you?" I said. "Jody doesn't want another dog. She wants Stinky."

I went out for a walk and left Zak on the computer. I found out later that he'd put a message on The Internet Pet Board. Once he gets an idea, there's no stopping him. He'd been asking for info about other dogs in the greyhound family.

THE INTERNET PET BOARD

TALK TO PET OWNERS AROUND THE WORLD!

Post your message on The Internet Pet Board:
Questions – jokes – photos –
fascinating facts – in fact, anything that
other pet lovers will find interesting.

Message from: Zak, Prestbury, England
Can anyone tell me about the different breeds found in the greyhound family?

Brian Brain, Montreal, Canada
Hi Zak
Hey fella! You're wrong to think there's a group of dogs called the "greyhound family".
Greyhounds belong to the "sighthound" family.
These are hounds that hunt with their eyes more than their noses! Experts reckon that a dog's sense of smell is 50,000 times greater than a human's. So think how good a sighthound's eyesight must be!

GREYHOUND POLISH GREYHOUND
BASENJI WHIPPET
SIGHTHOUND FAMILY
AFGHAN HOUND ITALIAN GREYHOUND PHARAOH HOUND

E. Rake, Malta

Take a look at my noisy Pharoah Hound, Big Ears. Perhaps Big Ears should be called Big Mouth 'cos he's always barking. In fact it's driving me barking mad! Mind you, he's got an interesting history. The Pharoah Hound was one of the greyhound-type dogs that the Ancient Egyptians loved to hunt with. Compare my picture of Big Ears with this ancient Egyptian statue of Anubis, God of the Dead and Embalming. Notice anything similar?

BIG EARS

ANUBIS

Yeah, my dog's ancestor was an Egyptian God! P.S. Does anybody have a sighthound that doesn't bark?

Lulu Kololo, Addis Ababa, Africa

Yes, my sighthound is a Basenji from central Africa. They're very strange sounding creatures because they don't bark, they YODEL! It's true. And they were bred to catch rats. Bentley, my Basenji, is clean,  intelligent and affectionate (but not to rats). Look at his beautiful curly tail. It might sound loopy but some Basenjis have two loops in their tail!

Luigi Teeni-Poochini, Turin, Italy

Beano, my Italian greyhound, is the smallest of all sighthounds – about the size of a cat but much thinner and lighter! My wife says he has total control over me. Ridiculous! Oops, better go. He's whining for his supper.

Willy Barkwright, Settle, England

Whippets are sighthounds too, you know. My little whippet, Sticky, is as swift as they come. Sticky may be small, but he's the fastest rabbit catcher I've ever

seen. Whippets are a bit like mini-greyhounds, intelligent dogs, but nothing can stop them when they spot a rabbit.

Up north, where I come from, whippets have been popular since the 19th century. A poor family with a whippet could send the dog off hunting and it'd bring back some extra meat for their tea. Families even raced their whippets against each other. In fact, they used to call whippets "the poor man's race horse".

Hanna Houndowska, Warsaw, Poland

Did you know there are also Polish greyhounds? They are called Chart Polskis. My hound is called Polly-Polskis and she has a lovely shiny coat. Yes, my Polish greyhound looks as if she's been "polished"!

Mustafa Brush, Herat, Afghanistan

Am I the only person with a hairy sighthound? I spend an hour a day brushing Hairy Harry my Afghan Hound. Originally they were bred in Afghanistan (amazingly) to catch leopards! Afghans are very intelligent but difficult to train. This is because of their hunting history. Apparently, they could outrun just about anything on rocky ground and often spent hours on their own tracking down a leopard. This made them cunning, independent free thinkers!

THE LEOPARD HAS FEW ENEMIES...

Hairy Harry has never even seen a leopard, but he's very independent. Like many Afghan Hounds, he only hears the commands that he wants to hear. Commands like, "Walkies!" and "Dinner!"

Chris Crossbreed, Essex, England

My dogs are Twiggy and Loggy. Twiggy is a thin Saluki/Whippet "longdog". (A longdog is a cross between two sighthounds.) Loggy's a sturdy collie/greyhound "lurcher". (A lurcher is a cross between a sighthound and any other type of dog.) Now you can impress your doggy friends because not a lot of people know this!

"I saw those messages, it's interesting stuff," Dad called out from the surgery.

"It might be interesting," I called back, "but I don't think Jody will want to read about other types of dog, just at the moment. I wish Zak wouldn't keep sticking his nose in."

"He's only trying to help," Dad put his head round the door. "Maybe you could suggest an older greyhound. A dog of eight or nine would probably be more interested in sleeping than chasing cats or going for long walks. You could. . ."

"Leave it, Dad. Please," I said quietly and tapped out an email to Jody.

THE INTERNET VET

From: Beth

Hi Jody

You must be feeling really miserable. I know how much you loved Stinky. Now you've lost your cat and your greyhound.

Zak thinks you should get another type of dog (you may have seen the Pet Board) and Dad suggests you get an older greyhound.

I can't think of much more to say except that I hope we can still be friends and keep in touch.

Love from Beth XX

The peace was shattered. "Hey Betts, Ethel and Dora have just arrived," Dad called out. "Can you help the old girls get their doddery dog out of the car, please?"

I switched off the computer. Oh well, I thought, life goes on.

Purr'fect Ending?

I helped Dotty, the ancient Dalmatian, out of the car and into Dad's surgery. Dotty wasn't the only one that needed help. Ethel and Dora both needed an arm to lean on as they wobbled their way from car to house. As we plodded up the drive I remembered an ad we'd put together a few weeks before.

Dotty's problem was easy to spot. The poor old thing had lumps under her skin. These fatty lumps (Dad says that vets call them lipomas) are usually found in older dogs. Dotty needed surgery to get rid of them and samples of the lumps were sent to a laboratory for testing. Dad's always sending stuff off for testing. He wanted to find out if the lumps were malignant. Malignant – yuk, I hate that word! If Dotty's lumps *were* malignant it meant that they could harm other parts of her body and maybe even kill her.

We called Ethel and Dora the "Wonderful Sisters". They preferred dogs to men, it seemed. Except for Dad. Wonderful Dad!

A week later he told them that Dotty could go home.

"Oh you are wonderful, Mr Kennel, what would we do without you?" they chanted in stereo.

"Er, yes, well," replied Dad, "I've removed Dotty's lumps. The lab tests are back and I'm pleased to say that they didn't show anything serious."

"Wonderful! Wonderful!" they echoed.

"And here's my bill for the treatment, ladies," Dad added.

"Ah yes, wonderful!" came their predictable response.

It had been an expensive operation but they both seemed happy after the week of waiting. And what a long week it had been. I'd spent most of it moping around. I just couldn't stop thinking about Jody, Stinky and Clint. Was Stinky unhappy? Had Clint returned? Was Jody miserable?

I was about to find out:

From: Jody
To: Beth

Hi Beth
I'm still shaking from everything that's been going on.

A couple of days after you last emailed me, I was up in my room when I heard the front door bell.

I heard Pop downstairs, talking to Mrs Lozinski from across the way. She sounded kind of upset so I ran down to see what was up. I couldn't believe my eyes. Dad was holding . . . CLINT! The poor cat was SO thin and weak looking. But he was alive.

Where had he been for the last ten days? Locked in Mrs Lozinski's garden shed, that's

where. It had happened accidentally and wasn't Mrs Lozinski's fault but she felt real bad about it. Clint seems OK. He's eaten loads and slept loads, too. Pop's real pleased to have his furry friend back!

Mrs Lozinski

SO STINKY HADN'T SCARED CLINT AWAY.

I always knew it but Pop wouldn't believe me. I had a lump in my throat when I asked Mom and Pop if Stinky could come home. Mom gave me a hug and said... YES. But only if Stinky was still there and the kennel boss agreed. Why wouldn't he? Stinky wasn't going to race again and we were offering to feed and look after her.

Mr Leech was out when we phoned the kennels so Pop left a message explaining everything.

The following morning I set off with Pop on the long journey. I sat in the back of the station wagon praying that Stinky would still be there.

We parked up and as we walked across the yard Mr Leech came striding towards us.

We'd had a wasted journey, he told us. Stinky had escaped and run off again. And even if the dog did turn up, he made it quite clear that she was his property, not ours.

Pop asked how a dog had managed to get out of the wired enclosure but Leech wasn't in the mood for a discussion and marched off to his office.

So there we stood in the yard, Pop looking shell-shocked and me in tears. There was nothing more we could do. Pop put his hand on my shoulder and we walked back to the station wagon.

A car pulled up beside ours and the driver got out. She must have thought Pop was one of the kennel workers. She'd come to pick a greyhound up. She asked if we knew where Mr Leech was, or maybe we could take her to the dog. The hound was called HONEY DANCER.

The name sent a shiver up my spine. What did this mean? Pop was silent for a few seconds. Then he smiled. It was as if everything had become clear to him. He said, sure he'd take her to Mr Leech. No problem.

We stepped into the kennel office. The colour drained from the Leech's face as he looked up to see the three of us standing there.

He told us to leave, but Pop said we weren't going nowhere. The creepy Leech had lied about Stinky escaping and Pop knew why. Leech had seen how fit and well Stinky looked when we'd brought her back. He'd realized she might be worth a few bucks and contacted Mrs Crook, the woman who'd bought Stinky before.

 Then Mrs Crook joined in. It was none of our business, she said. The dog belonged to the kennel, not us. Pop played his trump card. He told Leech to get Stinky immediately.

If he didn't, Pop would report him to the National Greyhound Association. Pop had been doing his homework. He'd been reading the NGA stuff that came with Stinky's details.

When a greyhound changes owners it has to be re-registered and given a new number. The NGA might be interested to hear that Leech hadn't been doing this. If he had, our search for Stinky would have led us to Mrs Crook's kennels, not Leech's. How many other poor hounds was he getting rid of like this? Then Pop questioned Mrs Crook. Had Stinky really escaped from her kennels? Or did she dump the greyhounds that didn't get fit enough to race again? The game was up and they knew it.

Leech left the office in silence. Two minutes later he returned with Stinky.

It was so great to see Stinky again. We had to endure a lot of sloppy licking and tail whipping.

There was nothing more to say. We left Leech, he was so mad at us, and headed home.

And now we are home, everything's just fine. When Stinky saw Clint she started wagging her tail. Clint wasn't quite as delighted to see Stinky, but, hey, he hasn't run off.

Pop's been coming out for walks. We really get to talk and he's looking almost as fit as Stinky! I think Mom approves. She says Stinky's been good for all of us.

Thanks again for all your help and also say a big thank you to your dad and Zak.

Write soon
Love Jody XX

P.S. Pop told the NGA about crooked Crook and the creepy Leech, anyway!

I ran into the surgery to tell Dad and Zak about Jody's email.

"Hey, Dad. . ." I stopped in mid sentence. Dad and Zak were trying to wrap an angry parrot, called Wingo, in a towel.

"I need to trim his beak," Dad gasped. "Hold him, Zak!"

It was a bit embarrassing. The worried owner was watching from the corner of the room. Parrots' beaks grow like our fingernails and need trimming down when they've become overgrown. I don't think Dad had done one recently. Earlier that day I'd caught him checking how to do it in a book.

Despite his research, things weren't going to plan. Poor Dad, he was looking a bit red in the face even before Wingo bit him. Now he was almost as red as his patient.

"Ouch!" he wailed, as the stressed bird flapped out of the towel and onto his shoulder. Then Wingo decided to celebrate his freedom by having a poo.

"I've only just got that wee stain out of my shirt," Dad moaned. "I don't know what's worse, parrot poo or cat pee."

Zak was looking thoughtful. "Er, parrot poo, I think." His tone was serious. "It smells worse and it shows up more on your shirt. You need a Parrot Poop Catcher, Dad. Remember that advertisement we did?"

INTERNET VET ADVERTISEMENTS

PURCHASE PET PRODUCTS FROM AROUND THE WORLD!

ATTENTION ALL PARROT KEEPERS!

Are your shoulders always covered in parrot poo? You need our new

PARROT POOP CATCHER!

* Attaches comfortably around your neck

* Comes in many poop-catching, sorry, eye-catching colours.

* Can hold up to 1kg (2lbs) of parrot poop

* Order today and we'll send you the beak, sorry, the bill.

POOP!

Dad told the owner to fit natural perches in Wingo's cage. Unlike most perches, which are straight and smooth, these are knobbly, like branches. Parrots can rub and sharpen their beaks on these just as they would in the jungle.

So it all got sorted out in the end. At last I was able to tell Dad and Zak the good news.

"I'm pleased it worked out," Dad breathed a sigh of relief. "And I'm also pleased to see you smiling again."

"Fantastic!" Zak said. "And it's given me a brill idea for our Greyhound File!"

I didn't have time to ask what the idea was. He disappeared up to his room mumbling something about biographies and digital data. We left him to it. He's happier on his own planet.

Dad gave me a hug. "This Internet Vet thing is working out quite well," he said. "And it was all your idea, Betts. What would I do without you?"

"Don't go soppy on me, Dad," I blushed. "Anyway, it's fun for us, too. We didn't know anything about greyhounds until all this started, now we know loads."

A few days later even Zak was flattering me.

"I've been working on that idea for the Greyhound File," he announced. "It'll look loads better with some of your drawings."

It certainly was one of Zak's better brainwaves. A brilliant way of telling people about greyhounds – how many need rescuing and what excellent pets they make! It kept us busy for the rest of the Easter holidays. And Jody helped too. After all, the Greyhound File was all about Stinky. . .

Pet on the Net

We at the Internet Vet are here to help you with your pet problems, but we also want to tell you about some of our most interesting cases. It's several months since Jody first wrote to us from the USA. She needed help with a greyhound she'd found, called Stinky. Since then, we've found out loads about greyhounds and we thought you might like to read about them too.

Every year, hundreds of thousands of greyhounds are bred around the world. They can live for about 14 years, but they only usually race for two to five years.

So what happens to them after that? It's a sad story. Tens of thousands of ex-racers are killed each year, because they're injured, or just didn't run fast enough!
But the good news is – greyhounds make brilliant pets! They're gentle with children and only need one walk a day. It's true – ask Jody!

Stinky was a racing greyhound with an injured leg. So how come she got lucky? Here's her story. . .

STINKY'S STORY

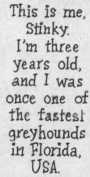

This is me, Stinky. I'm three years old, and I was once one of the fastest greyhounds in Florida, USA.

GOOD LOOKS

GOOD LEGS

LADY GRACE (MY MOM)

I come from good stock, Mom was a champ, too.

117

She stopped racing at three, and bred puppies 'til she was 12: too old to be useful any more.

ME, I'M THE ONLY GIRL

SNUB NOSES

MY UGLY BROTHERS

At eight weeks old we were taken away from Mom — and given tattoos! All racing greyhounds have them.

399A — MY MONTH AND YEAR OF BIRTH (MARCH 1999) AND ORDER IN THE LITTER — NO 1, OF COURSE! 4273 — MY LITTER NUMBER AND THE NUMBER OF MY KENNELS.

I was fastest even then.

At three months I started to grow in some funny places!

At four months I was fitted with a collar.

HONEY DANCER

You didn't think I'd race with a name like Stinky, did you?

At six months I sort of went to school to get ready for my first race.

LEARNING TO CHASE

A year later the big day arrived...

I ran round the track at breakneck speed.

A tight finish

I WON!

ME —
STARTING
TO CATCH UP

I was a star!

AND A STAR DESERVES
SOMETHING SPECIAL.

Soon I was the talk
of the track.

HONEY DANCER, MUTTER,
MUMBLE, HONEY DANCER...

Then one night something snapped in my leg.

I limped over to my trainer. He wasn't pleased at all!

Things got worse. I was taken to a strange place.

My owner shook hands with a woman then he left me behind.

She took me to her kennels

ONE WORRIED DOG!

I started to howl.

SHUT UP AND GET BETTER, OR YOU'RE OUTTA HERE, LADY

BUT MY LEG GOT WORSE...

She kept her promise...

MIDDLE OF NOWHERE

ME — VERY COLD!

This was some sort of mistake, right?
Wrong! I was useless, so I got chucked out.

I walked all night and managed to find some food.

SCRAPS

TWO WEEKS LATER

BONES SHOWING THROUGH

This was no way for a star to live.

But then I got lucky again!

JODY ME

So that's Stinky's story. Rescuing a dog is a big responsibility, but if your family all agree, why not rescue a greyhound? And you could be saving a life. You can be certain of one thing – any trouble you take to home a hound will be rewarded a hundred times over.

So that was it. I could tell you that we all lived happily ever after, but I was just about to turn the computer off when another email came through:

From: Billy Bong,
        Wollongong, Australia
To: The Internet Vet

G'day mate

Thanks for helping out with the frog prob. Anyway, I've been thinking I might have more luck with snakes. I managed to get this one cheap 'cos I think he's got something wrong with his tail. Is there a bone loose or something? It's making a real loud rattling noise. . .

THE INTERNET VET

Help!

Something's

eaten

my

hamster

Dear Internet Vet
My pet hamster, Eggs, is missing. He might have
been eaten by a snake called Sssid! Please help.
Mickey

What could we do? Well, we did discover why
rodents have such long teeth, how some lizards
lose their tails – on purpose, and what to do with
python poo. But had Sssid really eaten Eggs for
breakfast? Find out inside...

Look out for: *Help! My cat's too fat*

THE INTERNET VET

WIN PRIZES

WHY NOT VISIT OUR WEBSITE?

We're at:

WWW.INTERNET-VET.CO.UK

PET STUFF — Stacks of fascinating facts and other PET STUFF

WIN STUFF — Take part in our monthly competition and WIN STUFF!

BOOK STUFF — BOOK STUFF – the latest info on forthcoming titles

LINK STUFF — Check out other pet sites on the LINK STUFF page

HORRIBLE SCIENCE

**Also illustrated
by Tony De Saulles**